IT'S G...
FUI...

GW00870367

Contents

Horribilly's Music 2
By Michaela Morgan

Cooking with Horribilly 8

Jellyfish Stew 10
By Jack Prelutsky

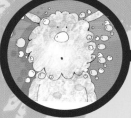
Soapy Steve 12
By Jess Mikhail

See you inside

Horribilly's Music

It was Music Week.

SCHOOL

School Hall ➡

Look at all these instruments!

We've got things to shake ...

Shake!

... and things to ding!

Ding!

4

This drum is perfect for you, Horribilly!

Yes!

I can play the big, big drum,
I know I can do it.
Bang Bang BANNNNNG goes
the big, BIG drum.
Yes! That's the way to do it!

The End

Cooking with Horribilly

9

Jellyfish Stew

Jellyfish stew,
I'm loony for you,
I dearly adore you,
oh, truly I do,
you're creepy to see,
revolting to chew,
you slide down inside
with a hullabaloo.

You're soggy, you're smelly,
you taste like shampoo,
you bog down my belly
with oodles of goo,
yet I would glue noodles
and prunes to my shoe,
for one oozy spoonful
of jellyfish stew.

Jack Prelutsky

Soapy Steve

Steve – a boy who turns into a Soapy Hero!

14

Yes! I am Dirty Doreen and I LOVE making things mucky!

Help! Help us!

As Steve thinks, lots of bubbles pop out!

Soon soapy bubbles are all over the bus.

Go away, Dirty Doreen!